Christmas Club
Payment

**7**

Due this week

Only

**1 2**

Days Left Before
Christmas

*Florist*

**Books by Peter Spier:**

The Fox Went Out on a Chilly Night
PETER SPIER'S MOTHER GOOSE LIBRARY
   London Bridge Is Falling Down!
   To Market! To Market!
   Hurrah, We're Outward Bound
   And So My Garden Grows
Of Dikes and Windmills
The Erie Canal
Gobble, Growl, Grunt
Crash! Bang! Boom!
Fast-Slow, High-Low
The Star-Spangled Banner
Tin-Lizzie
Noah's Ark
Oh, Were They Ever Happy!
Bored—Nothing to Do!
The Legend of New Amsterdam
People
PETER SPIER'S VILLAGE BOOKS
Peter Spier's Rain
Peter Spier's Christmas
PETER SPIER'S LITTLE BIBLE STORYBOOKS
PETER SPIER'S LITTLE ANIMAL BOOKS
The Book of Jonah
Dreams
We the People
Peter Spier's Advent Calendar

Published by The Trumpet Club
666 Fifth Avenue  New York, New York 10103
Illustrations copyright © 1983 by Peter Spier
address:  Doubleday, a division of the Bantam Doubleday Dell
Publishing Group, Inc., New York, New York.
ISBN: 0-440-84146-1
Reprinted by arrangement with Doubleday, a division of the
Bantam Doubleday Dell Publishing Group, Inc.
Printed in the United States of America
November 1989  10 9 8 7 6 5 4 3 2 · UPC

# Peter Spier's
# CHRISTMAS!

A TRUMPET CLUB SPECIAL EDITION